THE
EXISTENTIAL
COLORING BOOK

ISBN: 978-0-9816031-8-6

10 9 8 7 6 5 4 3 2 1

Printed in China

© 2014 Archie McPhee

THERE IS A LIFE, AND THERE IS A DEATH, AND THERE ARE BEAUTY AND MELANCHOLY BETWEEN.

- ALBERT CAMUS

YOU ARE FREE AND THAT IS WHY YOU ARE LOST.

- FRANZ KAFKA

DOSTOYEVSKY: WHAT'S WRONG WITH THIS PICTURE?

CAPTAIN

I LOOKED UP AT THE MASS OF SIGNS AND STARS IN THE NIGHT SKY AND LAID MYSELF OPEN FOR THE FIRST TIME TO THE BENIGN INDIFFERENCE OF THE WORLD.

- ALBERT CAMUS

© Archie McPhee

I HAVE AN EXISTENTIAL MAP. IT HAS "YOU ARE HERE" WRITTEN ALL OVER IT.

- STEVEN WRIGHT

MAN IS CONDEMNED TO BE FREE;
BECAUSE ONCE THROWN INTO THE WORLD,
HE IS RESPONSIBLE FOR EVERYTHING HE DOES.

- JEAN-PAUL SARTRE

© Archie McPhee

NO FINITE POINT HAS MEANING
WITHOUT AN INFINITE REFERENCE POINT.

- JEAN PAUL SARTRE

SINCE WATER STILL FLOWS, THOUGH WE CUT IT WITH SWORDS,
AND SORROW RETURNS, THOUGH WE DROWN IT WITH WINE,
SINCE THE WORLD CAN IN NO WAY SATISFY OUR CRAVINGS,
LET US LOOSEN OUR HAIR TOMORROW AND GO FISHING.

- LI PO

NIETZSCHE: WHAT'S WRONG WITH THIS PICTURE?

© Archie McPhee

LIFE BEGINS ON THE OTHER SIDE OF DESPAIR.

- JEAN-PAUL SARTRE

HELL IS OTHER PEOPLE.

- JEAN-PAUL SARTRE

© Archie McPhee

THE ARTIST'S JOB IS NOT TO SUCCUMB TO DESPAIR, BUT TO FIND AN ANTIDOTE FOR THE EMPTINESS OF EXISTENCE.

- WOODY ALLEN

EXISTENTIALIST CONNECT THE DOT

CONNECT THE DOT TO REVEAL THE TRUTH OF EXISTENCE.
(DRAW IN YOUR OWN DOT AND CONNECT IT TO CREATE THE ILLUSION OF MEANING.)

1
●

I EXIST, THAT IS ALL, AND I FIND IT NAUSEATING

- JEAN-PAUL SARTRE

© Archie McPhee

THERE IS A TERRIBLE EMPTINESS IN ME, AN INDIFFERENCE THAT HURTS.

- ALBERT CAMUS

EXISTENTIALIST WORD SEARCH

X X X X X X X X X

X X X X X X X X X

X X X X X X X X X

X X X X X X N X X

X X X X X X O X X

X X X X X X T X X

X X X X X X H X X

X X X X X X I X X

X X X X X X N X X

X X X X X X G X X

X X X X X X X X X

X X X X X X X X X

THIS IS A MIRROR. DRAW THE EMPTY ABYSS THAT STARES BACK AT YOU.

KNOW WHEN TO QUIT AND HAVE A COCKTAIL.

- ARCHIE MCPHEE

© Archie McPhee